Name: _____

Form: _____

Electrical Circuits

- Read, engage and learn!
- Full colour, illustrated Write Your Own Notes Booklet.
- Glossary, Memory Map, Active Learning Game & Flashcards.
- Ideal for ISEB 13+ Common Entrance and KS3 pupils.

This Oaka™ Books Write Your Own Notes Booklet goes hand in hand with the Active Learning Pack on this topic. The pack includes a Topic Booklet, an Active Learning Game and Question & Answer Flashcards.

Fresh Focus on Learning

Electrical Circuits Glossary

Ammeter: ....

Components: ....

Ampere (Amp): ....

Connect: ....

Battery: ....

Current: ....

Bulb (Lamp): ....

Electrical Cell (also called a cell): ....

Buzzer: ....

Electrical Insulator: ....

Cell (also called electrical cell): ....

Electricity: ....

Charge: ....

Energy: ....

Chemical Energy: ....

Fuse: ....

Circuit: ....

Hazard: ....

Electrical Circuits Glossary

Insulator: ....
....
....
....

Resistance: ....
....
....
....

Kinetic Energy: ....
....
....
....

Series Circuit: ....
....
....
....

Light Energy: ....
....
....
....

Static Electricity: ....
....
....
....

Lamp (Bulb): ....
....
....
....

Switch: ....
....
....
....

Metal: ....
....
....
....

Symbol: ....
....
....
....

Motor: ....
....
....
....

Transfer: ....
....
....
....

Negative: ....
....
....
....

Voltage: ....
....
....
....

Parallel Circuit: ....
....
....
....

Voltmeter: ....
....
....
....

Positive: ....
....
....
....

Wire: ....
....
....
....

Fill in the blanks using these words to help you...

electric current   strain   switch   energy   televisions   wire   torches
chemical   electrical   gravitational   chemical   changed   light
out   stored   electrical   lamp   thermal   series   kinetic   sound

1   What is Electricity?

- We have all seen **electricity** in action.

- ...., washing machines and .... all use .... **energy**.

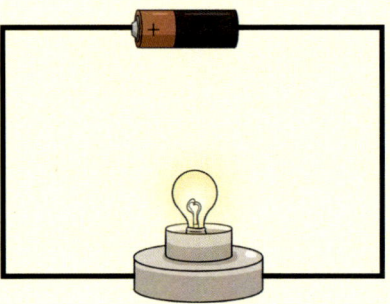

- This is a .... **circuit**, showing how a torch is connected.

2   Stored Energy

- **An** .... must move through the .... to make the .... glow.

- When we open the ...., the **lamp** goes ....!

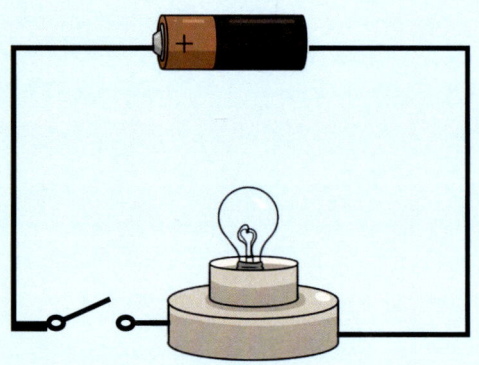

3   Types of Energy

Electricity is a form of ....!
Remember:

....
Energy

....
Energy

....
(heat) Energy

....
Energy

....
Energy

....
Energy
(movement)

....
Energy

4   Stored Energy

- Some **energy** has to be .... so that it is ready for use when we need it.

- .... **energy** is stored in **food**, **fuels** & in .... **cells**.

- A battery is made up of two or more .... **cells**, joined together.

   =

Batteries   contain   ....
Energy

5 Connecting Circuits

- Why do we use metal wires to **connect circuits**?

....
....
....

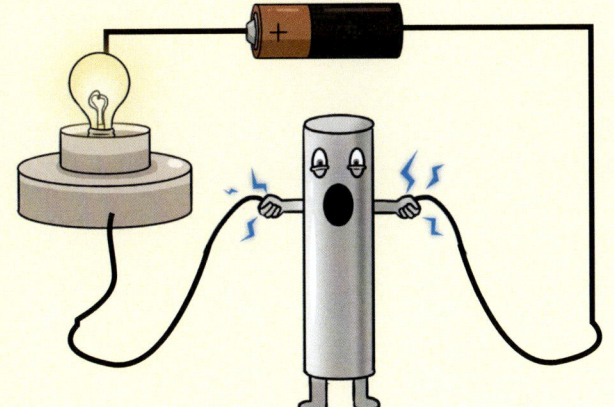

6 Connecting Circuits

- Some materials don't let electricity pass through them.

- These are **electrical** ....

- ...., rubber and .... are all good **electrical insulators**.

.... can't go through us!

7 Connected

- The wires must be connected to .... sides of ...., like **lamps** and **motors**.

- The .... goes through them.

8 Light Energy

- A **lamp** changes .... **energy** into .... **and** .... **energy** in a **circuit**.

Fill in the blanks using these words to help you...

electrons electricity all motor spark static kinetic circuit
current electrical jump out electrical battery charges chemical

9   Kinetic Energy

• A .... changes **electrical energy** into .... **energy** in a **circuit.**

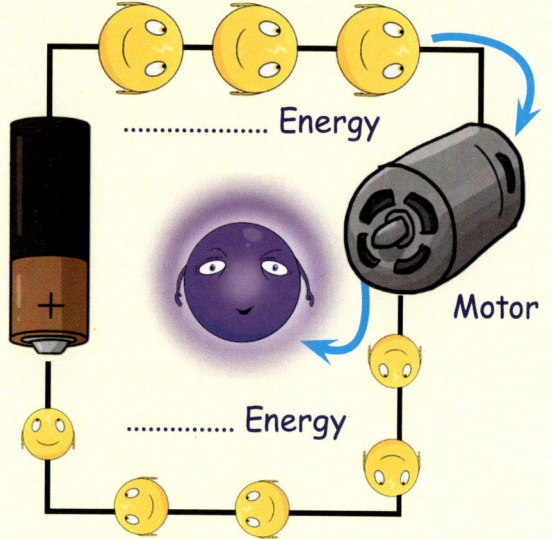

.... Energy

Motor

.... Energy

10   Series Circuit

• In a **series circuit**, if one **lamp** breaks then .... the **lamps** go ......!

• The .... **can't** go through all the lamps.
• The .... is **broken**.

11   Current

• When tiny .... **charges** move in the wire of a .... it is called a ....

• For an **electric** .... to move we need a complete ....

• We also need something to push the .... round.

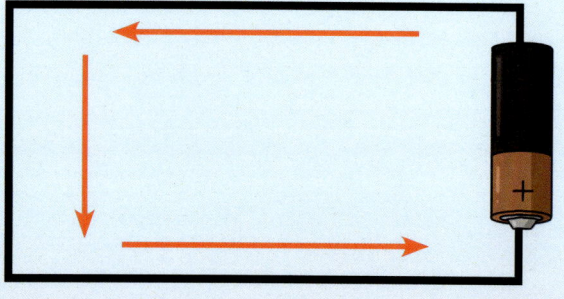

12   Electrons

• The .... **energy** in a ...., pushes these tiny **electrical charges** round the ....

The tiny .... in the wires are called ....

Fill in the blanks using these words to help you...

resistance I charges energy chemical ammeter V
amperes electrons electrical gain component current
voltage circuit volts battery charges amps lose voltmeter

13 Ammeter

- The **current** in a .... is measured using an ....

- The .... tells us how many .... are moving through a **circuit**.

- **Current** is measured in .... (............ for short) and we give it the symbol ...

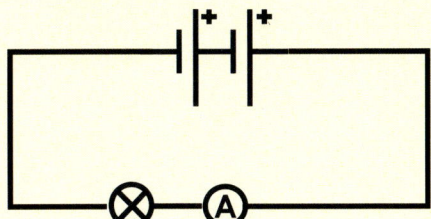

14 Losing Energy
(not tested for CE)

- .... tells us how much .... the **electrons** in the wire gain or lose across a ....

- **Electrons** .... **energy** across **batteries**.

- **Electrons** .... energy across .... like **lamps** and **motors**.

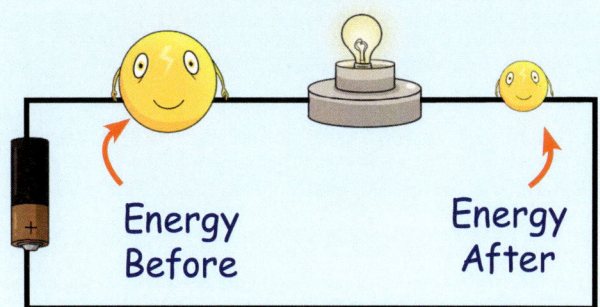

Energy Before   Energy After

15 Voltage
(not tested for CE)

- The **voltage** in a circuit is measured using a ....

- The **voltage** tells us how much .... the electrons have **before and after** a ....

- **Voltage** is measured in .... We use the **symbol** ......

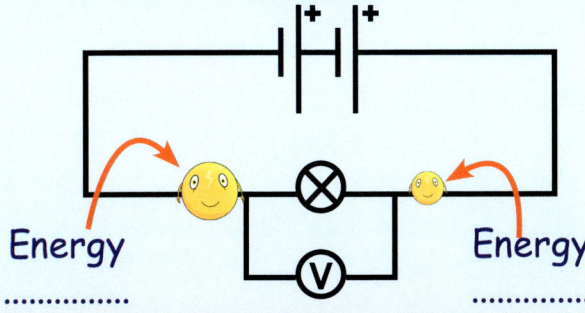

Energy ....   Energy ....

16 R.....................

- .... is a measure of how **hard** it is for **electrons** to move through .... in a circuit.

- When **electrons** move through **components** with high ...., like **lamps**, they lose a lot of their ....

- **Resistance** is measured in .... (Ω). We also use the **symbol** ....

17 Changing Energy

- When electrons move .... a lamp, some of their energy is lost as .... **energy** and .... **energy**.

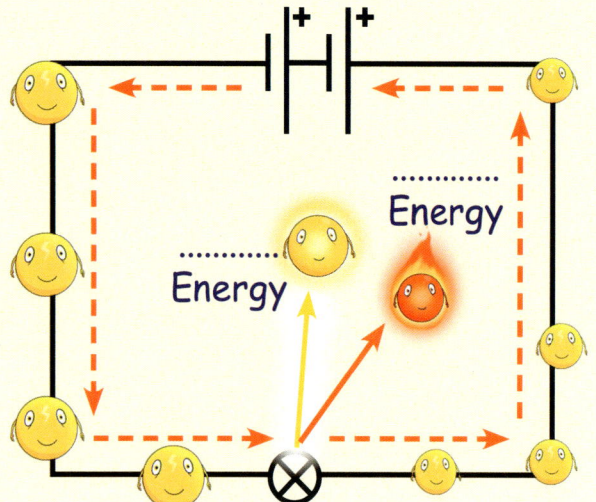

18 Work Out the Voltage
(not tested for CE)

- We can use equations to calculate **voltage**, **current** and **resistance**.

- **Voltage** = ... X ....

- If we know that the **Current** is 4, and the **Resistance** is 2, then

- **Voltage** = ... X ....

- **Voltage** = ... X ....

- **Voltage** = ...V

19 Use a Triangle
(not tested for CE)

- There are three equations, one to work out **voltage**, one for **current** and one for **resistance**.

- We can use a **triangle** to remember them.

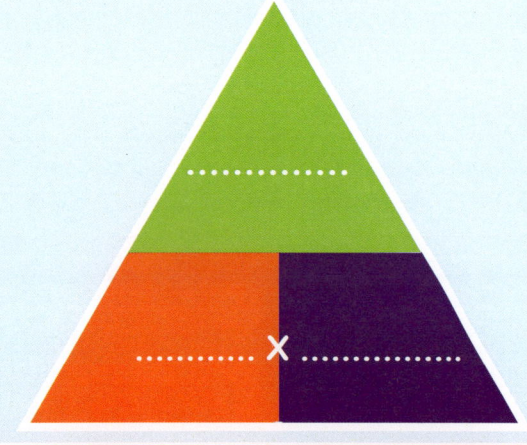

20 Voltage
(not tested for CE)

- Cover the value we want to calculate. If we want to know how to calculate **Voltage**:

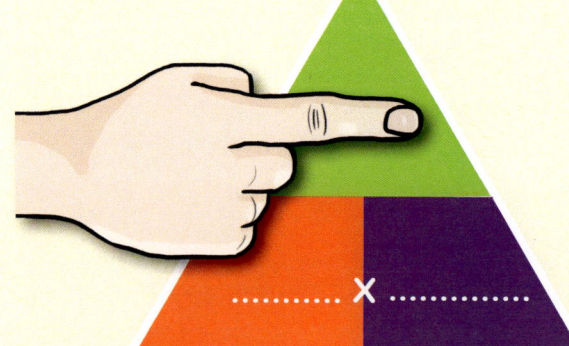

- **Voltage** = ... X ....

21   Current (not tested for CE)

- If we want to know how to calculate **current**:

- **Current** = ... / ....

22   Resistance (not tested for CE)

- If we want to know how to calculate **resistance**:

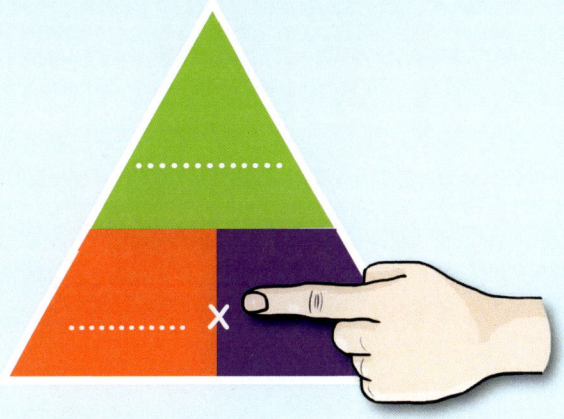

- **Resistance** = ... / ....

23   Let's recap...

- A **circuit** must be .... with no breaks.

- The .... **energy** in a **battery** pushes the charges (..................) round the ....

24   Let's recap...

Current

- **Voltage** tells us how much .... the **electrons** in the wire .... or .... across a **component**.

- The .... of **electrons** through the **circuit** is called an ....

- **Components** with high ...., slow the flow of ....

25 Transforming Energy

The .... **energy**, in the **circuit** can be changed (**transformed**) to .... **energy**, ... **energy** and .... **energy** by **components**.

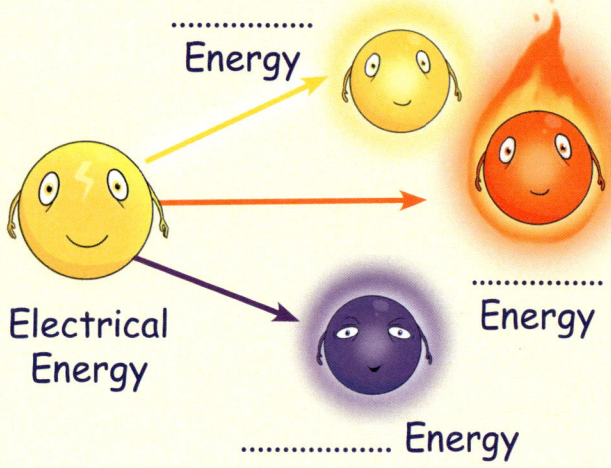

.... Energy

Electrical Energy

.... Energy

.... Energy

26 Definition: Voltage

You need to know these definitions:

Voltage (V) tells us how much .... the **electrons** in the wire gain or lose across a ....

5.0V

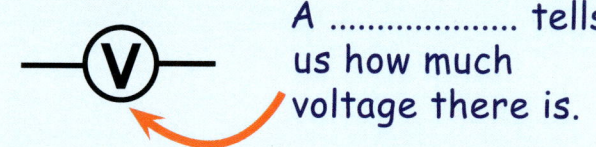

A .... tells us how much voltage there is.

27 Definition: Current

• When .... move round the wire of a .... it is called a .... (I).

28 Definition: Resistance

• **Resistance** (R) is a measure of how .... it is for **electrons** to move through .... in a ....

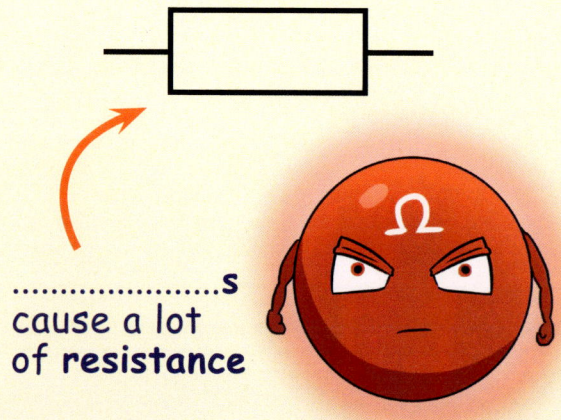

......................s cause a lot of **resistance**

Fill in the blanks using these words to help you...

battery   relay   wire   switch   cell   terminals   bulb   buzzer
diode   resistor   fuse   motor   push-button switch   ammeter
reed switch   variable resistor   conductors   semiconductor

Using Symbols

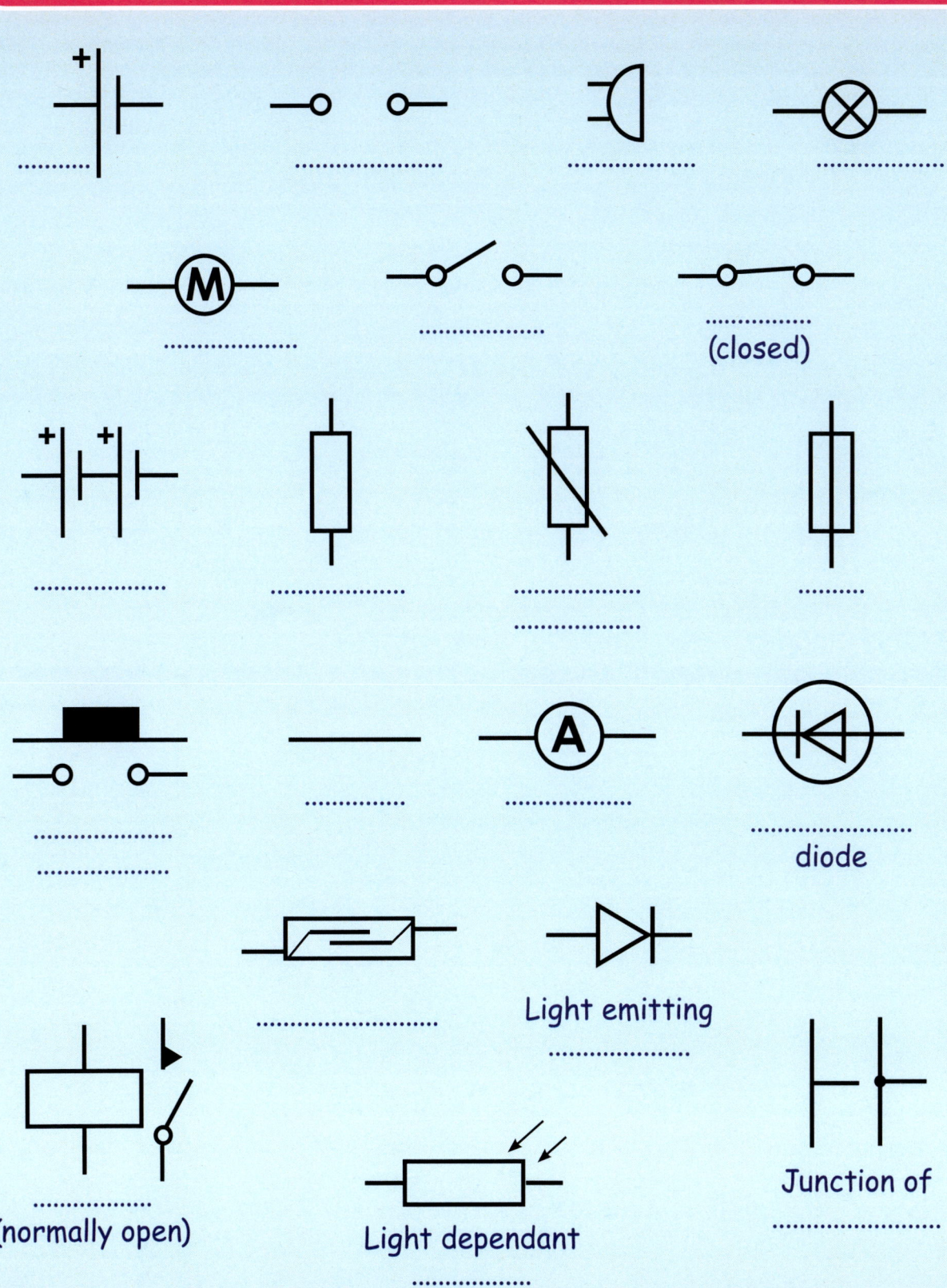

....

....

....

....

....

....

.... (closed)

....

....

....
....

....
....

....

.... diode

....

Light emitting
....

(normally open)

Light dependant
....

Junction of
....

Fill in the blanks using these words to help you...

toggle positive same chemical not metal one electrons reed
batteries open push circuit negative more cell cannot

29   The Wire

- Wires are made of .... They are full of the tiny **charges** that we call ....

- The .... are there all the time. They do .... get used up.

- .... give .... **energy** and .... them round the wires in a circuit.

30   The Cell

- The **cell** stores .... **energy**.

- The .... **energy** is used to push .... through the ....

- The **cell** has a .... terminal and a .... terminal.

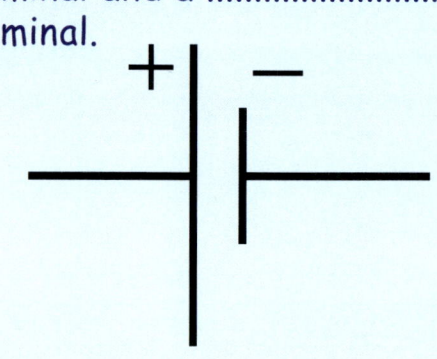

31   Batteries

- **Batteries** are made from .... than one .... joined together.

- **Cells** and **batteries** only push in .... **direction**. When you join them together, they must always point in the .... **direction**.

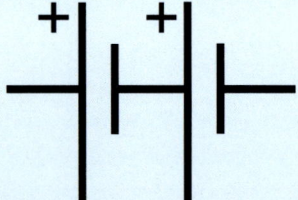

- The .... end of one **battery** connects to the .... end of the next **battery**.

32   Switches

- If the switch is ...., the battery .... push electrons round the ....

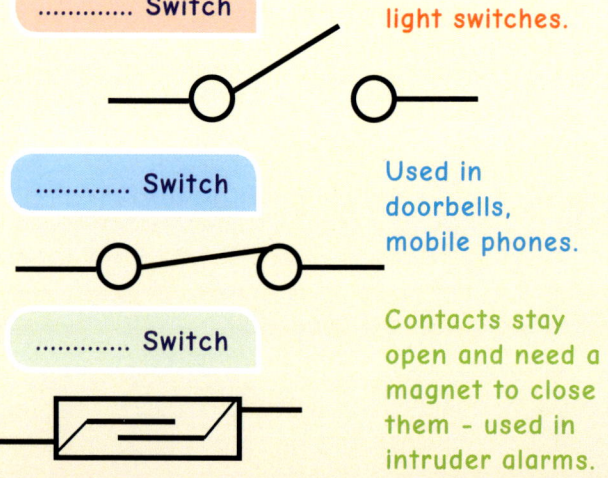

.... Switch   (SPST) used in light switches.

.... Switch   Used in doorbells, mobile phones.

.... Switch   Contacts stay open and need a magnet to close them - used in intruder alarms.

Fill in the blanks using these words to help you...

hard   motor   light   higher   large   direction   resistance   kinetic   resistor
thermal   large   resistors   current   other   electrons   energy   electrical

33   Lamps (Bulbs)

- **Lamps** have very high ....

- It is .... for the battery to push .... through the lamp.

- As the **electrons** are pushed through, lots of .... is **transformed** to .... and .... **energy**.

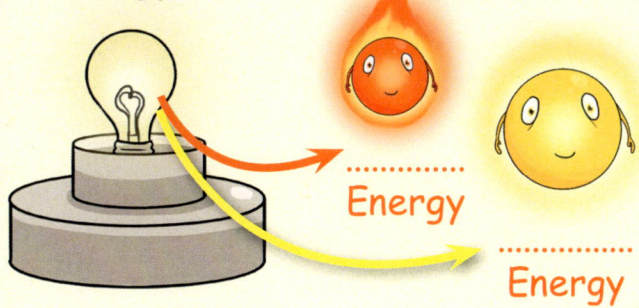

.... Energy

.... Energy

34   Motors

- As .... **energy** moves through a **motor**, it is transformed to .... **energy** (**movement energy**).

- **Batteries** only push **electrons** in one ....

- If you swap the terminals on the battery, the .... will spin the .... way!

35   Resistors

- .... make it difficult for **batteries** to push **electrons** round the circuit.

- The .... the **resistance**, the **smaller** the current.

- **Remember** that .... is **electrons** being pushed around a **circuit**.

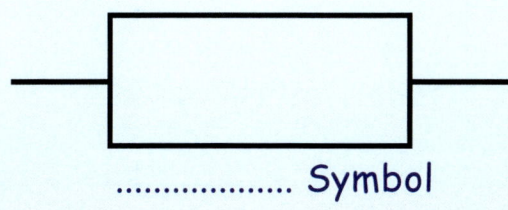

.... Symbol

No Resistance

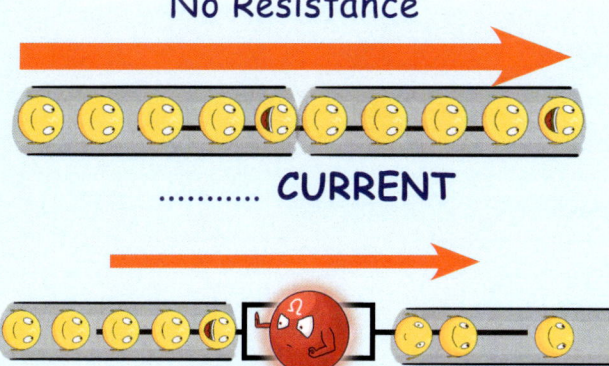

.... CURRENT

Smaller Current

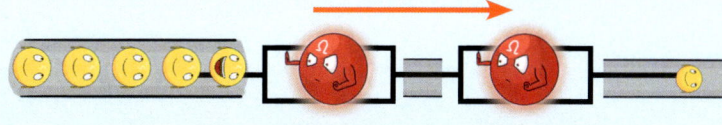

Very Small Current

36   .... Resistors

- With some **resistors** we can change their **resistance**. These are called .... resistors.

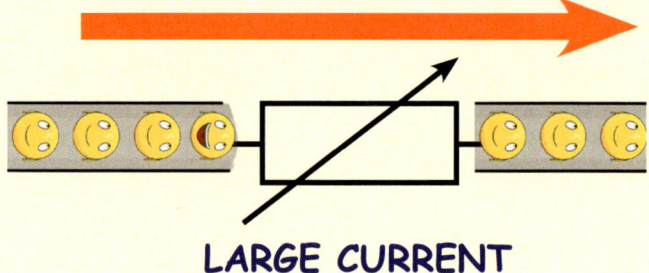

LARGE CURRENT

Lots of Resistance = ... Current

.... Resistance = Large Current

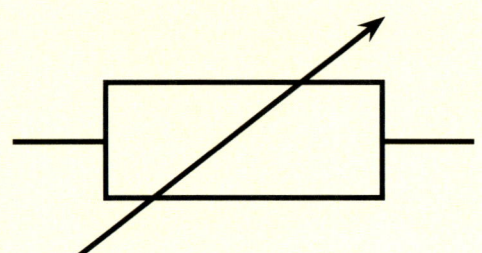

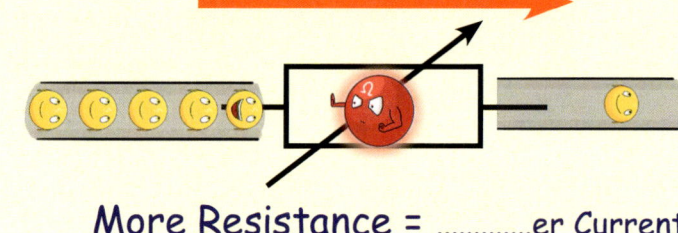

More Resistance = ...er Current

37   Circuits in Action

- This is a .... **circuit**. All the .... are connected in a .... loop.

- The **battery** uses its .... **energy** to push .... round the **circuit**.

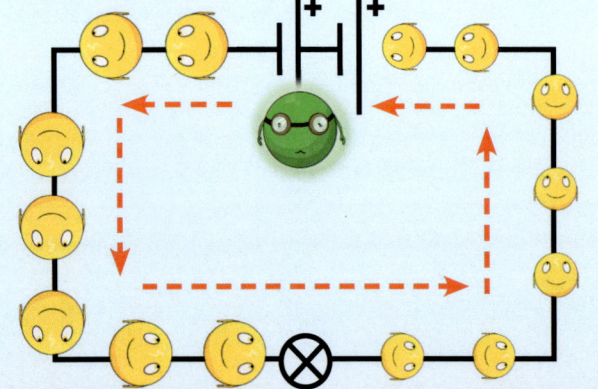

38   Circuits in Action

- The .... connect the **circuit**. **Electrons** in the **wire** are pushed by the ....

- The **lamp** transforms .... **energy** to .... and .... energy

Get moving!

39 Switches

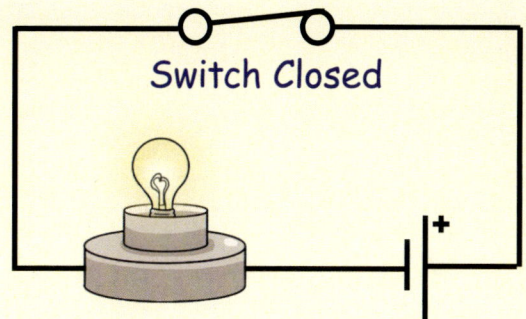

Switch Closed

When the .... is closed, the **lamp** lights up straight away.

Don't Forget!

• The **wire** is full of .... The **electrons** don't come from the **battery**. They are ... the wire. The **battery** just .... them.

40 More Voltage

• More **batteries** = more ....

• More push = higher ....

• Higher **voltage** = more ....

• More **energy** = ... **lamp**!

41 Transformation

• **Lamps** .... electrical energy

to **light** and **thermal energy**.

• If you put .... **lamps** into a series circuit, the **electrical energy** is .... out between them.

• There is .... **energy** available for each **lamp**.

• The **lamps** are ....

Fill in the blanks using these words to help you...

chemical voltmeter parallel component 9.0 share electrons
4.5 hard gained lose changed light energy not
battery lamp thermal two each twice energy

42 Voltage in Circuits

- We measure the **voltage** in a circuit using a ....

- Remember: **voltage** tells us how much .... the **electrons**, in the wire gain or lose across a ....

- Two **lamps**, in a **series circuit**, have to .... the **voltage**.

- The .... has to push .... through both.

- This is twice as .... as pushing .... through one **lamp**.

4.5V   4.5V

I've got to work .... as hard with .... lamps to light!

9.0V

43 Voltage in Circuits

- The **voltmeter** by the battery tells us how much .... the **electrons** have .... from the **battery**. (........ Volts in the diagram).

- The **Voltmeter by the** .... tell us how much .... the **electrons** .... at each **lamp** (............ Volts).

44 Flat Battery

- The **battery** will keep pushing the **electrons** in the wire until all of its .... **energy** has been **changed** to .... **and** .... **energy** at the **lamps**.

Don't forget:

- **Voltmeters** must be connected to .... side of a ....

- We say the **voltmeter** is connected 'in ....'

45 **Current in Circuits**

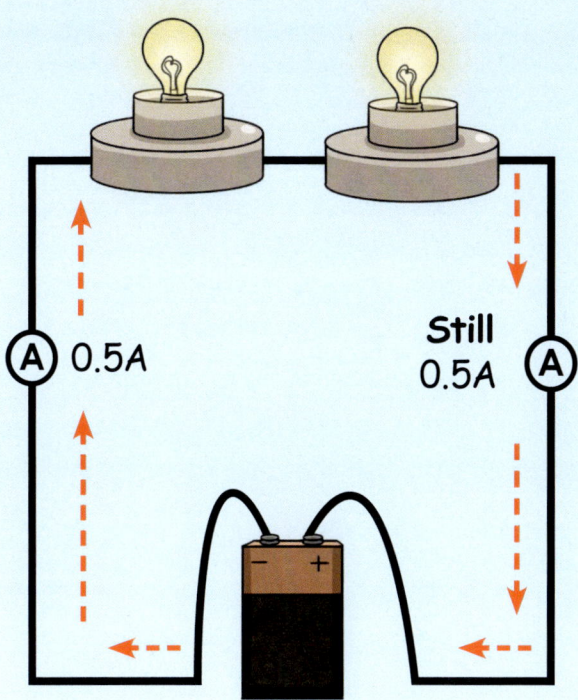

- We measure the **current** in a circuit using an ....

- Remember: the .... measures the **charges** (.................) moving through a **circuit**.

- The .... is the .... at all points in a **series circuit**.

- The .... (the moving **electrons**) is **not** used up.

- **Energy** from the moving .... is changed to heat and light energy.

46 **Resistance in Circuits**

- Remember: **resistance** is a measure of how .... it is for **electrons** to .... through .... in a **circuit**.

- We can **calculate** the **resistance** of each **lamp** using the triangle.

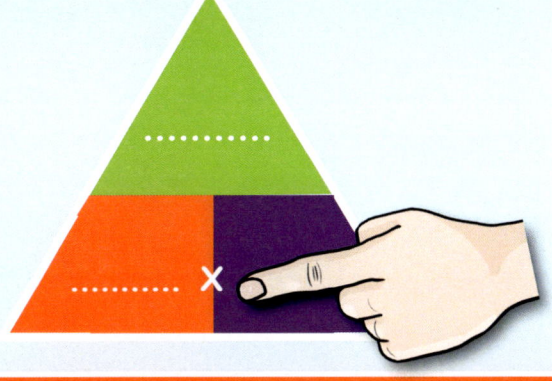

47 **Resistance in Circuits**

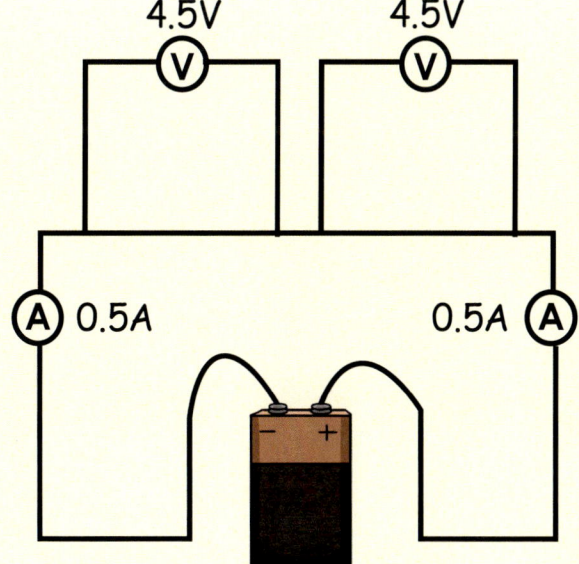

- Resistance = Voltage / Current
- Resistance = ... / ....
- Resistance = ... Ω

48   Parallel Circuits

- **Parallel circuits** are made up of .... or more ....

- Each loop is a complete ....

- Each .... can work on its ....

- The **current** is .... up between each **circuit**.

- .... **lamps** in this **circuit** are bright.

- Set up this **circuit** and measure the **voltage** across each **lamp!**

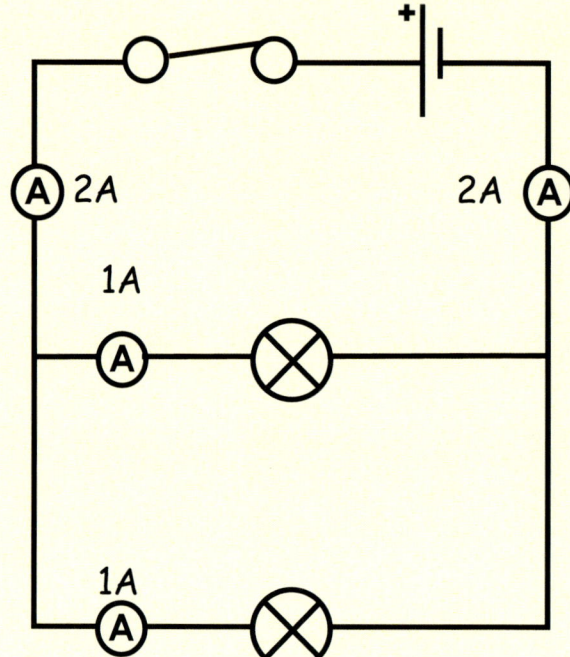

49   Parallel Circuits

- If there are ...... or more lamps in one circuit it, they will all go out if one ....

- If a lamp breaks all the .... flows through the other circuit so the .... stays on.

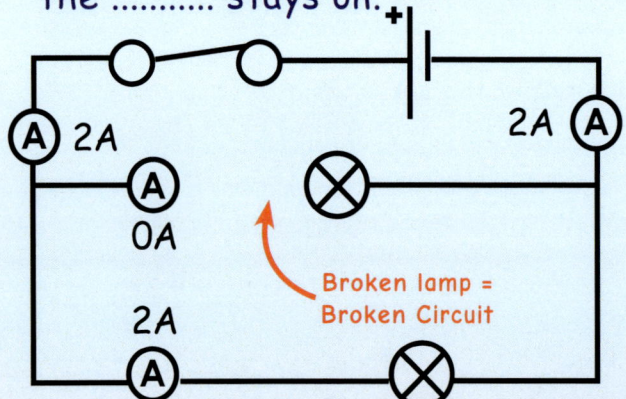

Broken lamp = Broken Circuit

- .... **circuits** are used in .... tree lights. If one **lamp** goes out, the others stay on.

- **Parallel circuits** are used in .... If one light goes out, the others stay ....

- The .... in each loop get the .... **voltage** (push) from the **battery.**

Fill in the blanks using these words to help you...

short   battery   hot   fuses   current   circuit   Amps   5A
13A   broken   protect   damaged   fuse   wire   high
components   blown   easiest   fires

50 Short Circuits

- Electricity takes the .... route in a circuit.

- A short .... happens when the .... flows round the circuit but does not go through any ....

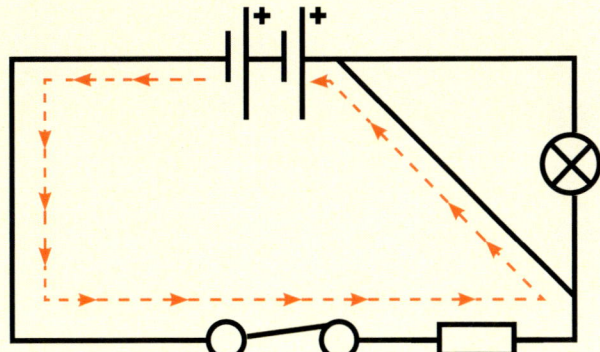

51 Fuses

- **Fuses** .... us. They stop appliances getting .... if too much .... flows through them.

- Inside a .... there is a piece of ....

- If the **current** gets too ...., the .... gets hot and melts. The **circuit** is ....

- We say the **fuse** has ....!

52 Fuses

- Different types of .... can carry different amounts of **current** (................).

- Common **fuse** ratings are: 1A, 3A, ... and ....

- The **fuse** rating should be higher than the .... in a ....

- A **circuit** that has 10A flowing through it should use a .... **fuse**.

53 Danger!

- A .... circuit means too much current will flow.

- It can make a .... or appliance ....

- It can cause electrical ....

Fresh Focus on Learning

About Oaka Books

Children learn best when they are engaged...

Our aim is to help children enjoy learning by making it fun! That way they will succeed.

Following Common Entrance and National Curriculum guidelines for KS3.

Design and layout of our books follow guidelines from the British Dyslexia Association.

Three Easy Steps

Read: the easy to follow bullet point Topic Booklet.

Engage: Play the Active Learning Game.

Learn: When you understand the topic, test yourself using the Write Your Own Notes Book. You can use the Topic Booklet to help if you get stuck.

One (short) Topic at a time:

For some students, a big book is a big turn off. That's why we focus on one topic at a time. Short and to the point.

Reading Age

This booklet is suitable for children with a reading age of 10 ½ years.

Topic Packs for KS1, KS2 & KS3 Include:

History
Geography
Chemistry
Biology
Physics

Please visit www.oakabooks.co.uk for more information about forthcoming titles

© Copyright 2017 Oaka Books. All rights reserved.
Written by Stuart Lawes, BSc, PGCE. Illustrations by Laurence Andrew Page.

First paperback edition printed 2014 in the United Kingdom.
A catalogue record for this book is available from the British Library.

ISBN 978-1-909892-52-1
This Write Your Own Notes Booklet may be photocopied for multiple use.
The accompanying Topic Booklet, Active Learning Game and question cards are not allowed to be copied without prior written permission from Oaka Books. Email: info@oakabooks.co.uk.

Designed, set and published by Oaka™ Books.

To order other titles from Oaka™ Books, please email info@oakabooks.co.uk or visit www.oakabooks.co.uk, or phone: +44 (0) 2392 388519.

Acknowledgements
Our huge thanks go to the many teachers who have been involved in the development of this series of learning guides. Special thanks to Joy Gardiner, for producing hundreds of illustrations, to Kate Doehren, for her enthusiasm and invaluable assistance to my wonderful daughter Sophie, for being the inspiration for the books and, of course, to Charlie, for believing in them.

ISBN 978-1-911189-87-9

CE/KS3
Electrical Circuits
Write Your Own Notes Booklet

ISBN 978-1-909892-52-1   Produced in association with Kate Doehren, MA Ed, B.Ed Hons, RSA Dip, Sp LD/Dyslexia
Head of Learning Support, Hurstpierpoint College
© Copyright Oaka™ Books 2017